MRS. POTTS FINDS
Thanksgiving

A story inspired by Dickens' classic, *A Christmas Carol*

ALICE K. BOATWRIGHT
Illustrated by Jan L. Waldron

Firefly Ink Books
Seattle, Washington 98155
www.fireflyinkbooks.com
Book design by Ampersand Bookery

SUMMARY: The miserly Mrs. Potts rediscovers the meaning of Thanksgiving with the help of a stray cat, in this story inspired by Charles Dickens' *A Christmas Carol*.

ISBN 979-8-9864344-1-4 (paperback edition)
ISBN 979-8-9864344-0-7 (hardcover edition)

For Jim,
who roasted the turkey while I wrote this story,

and for Bill,
who meowed in the night.

AKB

For David with love,
and to the grandkiddos we love so much.

JLW

1

A Lump of Newspapers

ON THE NIGHT before Thanksgiving, Martha Potts worked late. She had a report to finish – and besides, she wasn't in a hurry to get home. She had no plans for the holiday.

At five o'clock, her assistant Clara Thigg had come to her door, already wearing her coat.

"Are you sure you don't mind my leaving now, Mrs. Potts?" she asked timidly. Clara's daughter Abby was at home sick. Or so she said. It seemed to Mrs. Potts that Clara's child was sick an awful lot – especially around holidays.

"I do mind, but I said you could go," said Mrs. Potts in a grumpy voice. "So, go – just be sure to be here on time on Friday."

"Yes, Mrs. Potts," said Clara. "Happy Thanksgiving," she called, but Mrs. Potts was adding a column of figures and did not reply.

"Good night! Happy Thanksgiving!" her coworkers called to each other as they hurried off with their shopping lists and recipes. The stairwell echoed with their cheerful voices, and then the building fell silent.

Mrs. Potts sat hunched over her computer, deep in thought. It was really very important that she finish her report – hundreds of thousands of dollars in business depended on it. For several hours, her fingers flew across the keyboard, and she hardly even looked up to take a drink of water. It was nearly midnight when she turned off her computer, stretched, and put on her coat to go home.

Her footsteps rang out sharply as she went down the stairs and crossed the silent lobby, locking the doors behind her. The streets were quiet too. Mrs. Potts walked with a firm step and a tight hold on her purse as she crossed the parking lot to her car. She was not afraid. She had lived in the city all her life, and she knew how to take care of herself.

She was opening her car door when she noticed a sign on what looked like a lump of garbage and newspapers. It was a crudely painted piece of cardboard that said: "Happy Thanksgiving." As she stared at it, the lump moved and looked at her. Mrs. Potts was so startled that she dropped her keys. The lump was not a lump. It was an old woman.

2

What's the world coming to? she thought as she hastily picked up the keys.

The woman said nothing – and Mrs. Potts tried to avoid meeting her gaze. She did not believe in giving money to beggars. She gave to the poor through United Way.

Safely locked in her car, she found herself shivering. She hadn't realized it was so cold. She turned on the heat, then drove quickly through the dark streets.

On her way home she passed a strip of stores already decorated for Christmas, a brightly lit all-night diner, and a tall dark church with a sign on its basement door saying "Free Thanksgiving Dinner – 1 P.M." She was surprised to see that a line of people had already formed. Men, women, and children were huddled against the wall waiting for tomorrow's dinner. Mrs. Potts shivered again. She would need some hot milk before bed.

Finally, she reached her own neighborhood – a part of the city where large Victorian houses had been turned into apartments. Mrs. Potts had once lived in a house herself, but that was before her husband died and her daughter moved to New York. Now she had three rooms and that, she told herself, was quite enough to take care of. She preferred to put her money into stocks and bonds, not housing.

Once inside, she turned on all the lights, even before she took off her coat. Her little apartment was warm and tidy, and she was glad to be able to take off her shoes and settle down in front of a late news program. The news was bad, of course. Unemployment was rising; across the world people were fighting; storms were predicted.

What's the world coming to? Mrs. Potts wondered again. But she was so tired she had trouble following the stories and soon fell asleep.

2

A Meow in the Night

A YOWLING AND MEOWING soon woke her up. The noise was so loud Mrs. Potts thought the animal must be right in the room with her. "What a racket!" she muttered, slipping into her shoes, and going to the window.

She peered into the dark and hissed: "Quiet!"

When there was no response, she closed the window, satisfied that she had handled the crisis. But she had no sooner pulled the curtains than the yowling and meowing started again.

"Be quiet!" Mrs. Potts said, throwing open the window again. This time the meowing continued until she had located its source.

A scrawny little cat was stuck on the porch roof next door.

Now how did that get there? she wondered. And why doesn't someone let it in?

Then she remembered that she'd seen the owners leave for the holidays that morning.

Just like people today! she thought. *What's the world coming to?*

The cat looked down at her and meowed pitifully. It was cold and hungry, no doubt.

Mrs. Potts slammed down the window and tried to remember where her superintendent kept a ladder. Since she clearly wasn't going to have any peace until she got the cat down, she might as well get right to it.

She found the ladder in a storage shed behind the house. I hope no one calls the police, she thought, as she began to climb to the porch roof. But she needn't have worried. All the houses around her were dark and silent; only the cat paid any attention to what she was doing. He ran to her when she called him and clung to her shoulder with cold little paws as she carried him down.

"Now what?" she said to the creature when they were safely back in her apartment. "I suppose we could both use some hot milk." The cat meowed and rubbed against her ankles as she got out the saucepan.

"Beggar," she said, opening the refrigerator, where she found a little leftover chicken soup in a bowl. Perhaps the cat would prefer that.

Mrs. Potts watched as the cat hungrily lapped up the warm soup. When she was young, she had always had cats, and she'd been completely devoted to them. But this one looked like it had never had a home.

When the cat was finished eating and had given himself a thorough bath, he didn't look half bad, Mrs. Potts thought. He was a tuxedo cat – black with a white bib, white paws, and long white whiskers.

She picked him up and settled him on her lap. Right away he began purring. Mrs. Potts laughed and then coughed. It had been such a long time since she laughed that the sound embarrassed her.

"I suppose you're proud of yourself for finding a warm place to spend the night?" she said sternly.

The cat looked at her with his big yellow eyes and stretched himself up to her chin.

"Aren't you the little hugger," said Mrs. Potts. And then she realized she had just found his name.

3

The Smell of Turkey

WHEN MRS. POTTS woke up again, she was confused. She was still in her chair in San Francisco, but she had been dreaming that she was at her parents' home in Pennsylvania, and all her relatives were there for Thanksgiving dinner. The house smelled of turkey and potatoes, pumpkin and onion, bread and spices. The kitchen was crowded with aunts cooking and chopping and stirring, while her mother directed them waving a big wooden spoon. Her father and uncles were in the living room smoking pipes while they told each other stories. Her cousins were outside playing tag and kicking up the dead leaves.

Mrs. Potts was hiding from all the noise and confusion under the piano with her cat. She would have stayed there all day if she could, but her stomach growled at the good smells, and finally her mother called: "Martha! Martha! Where are you, Martha?"

That was when Mrs. Potts woke up. Her mother's voice was ringing in her ears, and she could still smell the roasting turkey. It was only a dream, she told herself sharply. But the growling of her stomach wasn't a dream; she was hungry.

Mrs. Potts went into her tiny kitchen, carrying the cat on her shoulder. She opened the refrigerator hopefully but it contained only a quart of milk, a carton of yogurt, mustard, and some wilted lettuce.

"Looks like that soup was the only good thing we had, Hugger," she said.

Mrs. Potts ate a few spoons of yogurt, but she couldn't forget that smell of roasting turkey, and she wanted real food.

I suppose it's not too late, she thought. "You'd like some turkey, wouldn't you?" she said to Hugger.

He circled her ankles and sat down on her foot.

Mrs. Potts decided that meant yes, so she got her biggest purse, tucked the cat into it, put on her coat, and went out to shop.

No other cars were on the road, and most stores and houses were completely dark, but the all-night grocery was brightly lit, waiting for customers. As she hurried into the store, a sleepy clerk looked up from his magazine and yawned.

"Do you have any turkeys left?" Mrs. Potts called to him anxiously.

"You must be kidding, lady. Today's Thanksgiving," he said.

Mrs. Potts took a cart anyway and went straight to the meat section. There in a long row were piles of hamburger, chops, roasts, chickens, hams – and then a big empty space where the turkeys should have been.

Mrs. Potts almost cried out her disappointment, until she noticed an enormous package wrapped in white paper stuck down among the legs of lamb, as if someone had decided at the last minute not to take it.

Surely it was – she hurried over to examine it – yes! It was a turkey! An awfully large turkey, she noted, as she heaved it into her shopping cart, but "Beggars can't be choosers," she told Hugger.

Now that she had her turkey, it was marvelous how she could recall all the other necessities. She rushed up and down the aisles piling the cart with stuffing mix, chest-

11

nuts, celery, onions, potatoes, cranberries, peas, pumpkin, butter, eggs, milk, sugar, flour, lard, and spices.

The cashier leapt to his feet when she rolled up to his register. "Gee, lady. You sure know how to miss the crowds. Looks like you're going to have a great dinner!"

"We most certainly are," said Mrs. Potts, giving him a ten-dollar tip. "Happy Thanksgiving," she said, with a wave.

And she was sure, as she climbed into the car, that she heard him call back: "Happy Thanksgiving!"

4

A Message for Mrs. Potts

AT HOME, SURROUNDED by her purchases, Mrs. Potts thought she had made a big mistake.

"Of all the foolish ways to waste a good night's sleep!" she said to Hugger.

She was very tired now, but it was almost morning. If she went to sleep, she might miss Thanksgiving completely. So, she started cooking instead.

Mrs. Potts had not done more than heat a dinner in the microwave for so long that she wasn't sure where to find anything in her own kitchen anymore.

The measuring cup was full of spoons and the flour sifter had a hole in it. The roasting pan turned out to be at the back of the broom closet. When she was pulling it out, she lost her balance and accidently knocked over a stack of books on saving money.

The books had been piled on a small bureau, and now that they were on the floor, she could see that her telephone had been buried underneath them. It said she had four messages.

Mrs. Potts was amazed. She couldn't remember the last time she'd received a call at home. She didn't have any friends, and she'd lost touch with her family – even her daughter. Friends were too nosy, always wanting to give you advice, and her family – well, they were great ones for borrowing money. She wanted no part of that.

Nevertheless, she had received four calls.

"Wrong number, no doubt," she said, but she checked the messages anyway.

The first one was almost a month old.

There was a pause, then a cheerful voice said:

"Hi, Mom! It's Lucy. I think it's time we talked. Harry and I are fine, and we'd love to have you come for Thanksgiving. Please give me a call." Beep!

The second message was from Lucy too.

"Mom, did you get my message? Please let me know if you can come for Thanksgiving. We've got plenty of room." Beep!

Even before it came on, Mrs. Potts could guess what the third message would say:

"Mom, please call me. It's been such a long time since we talked." Beep!

And finally:

"Well, Mom, I guess we won't see you for Thanksgiving. How about Christmas?" Beep!

The sound of her daughter's voice gave Mrs. Potts an unpleasant pinched feeling in her chest. They had not spoken for several years. Not since Lucy dropped out of law school to become an artist and ran off to New York with a no-good musician. At least that's how Mrs. Potts thought of him. The fact that she had heard some of his tunes on the radio did not change her mind one bit. Neither one of them had real jobs. She was sure they expected her to die and leave them her fortune.

"Go to New York for Thanksgiving indeed!" Mrs. Potts said indignantly. "Don't they know some people have to earn a living? They probably just wanted someone to take them out to dinner!" she told Hugger. But her hand trembled – just a little – as she erased the messages and stacked the books back on the bureau.

5

Lost in New York

ONCE THE TURKEY was in the oven, Mrs. Potts decided to lie down, just for a few minutes. Hugger thought this was a good idea too. He curled himself right under her chin and soon they were both asleep.

This time Mrs. Potts dreamed that she was in New York. She had arrived in the middle of the night, and her purse and all her belongings had been stolen.

She wandered the streets with no idea where to go. She couldn't even remember the name of Lucy's no-good husband to call for help. Finally, she had gone to sleep under a pile of newspapers.

In the morning she was awakened by a little girl who looked just like Lucy! She was even wearing the Navy coat with gold buttons that Mrs. Potts had bought her one winter.

"Are you hungry?" the little girl asked. She had blue eyes and long dark braids.

Mrs. Potts was too cold to say anything. She just stared.

"Come with me!" said the child, holding out her hand.

Without thinking, Mrs. Potts got up and took the girl's hand.

"Look, Mama, I brought another guest for dinner," the girl said, as she led Mrs. Potts into a big church basement filled with people. At one end of the room, a man was playing music and people were singing. At the other end, several women presided over a long table laden with food. The warmth and good smells made Mrs. Potts dizzy.

"Have a seat, dear," said her own daughter, who smiled without recognizing her. "We're very glad you're here and hope you'll come back for Christmas too."

Mrs. Potts was so angry that Lucy didn't recognize her that she sat there scowling until the child brought her the biggest plate of food she'd ever seen. It smelled so delicious, she had to smile, and she was just about to begin eating when she woke up.

"My dinner! Where'd it go?" she said, knocking Hugger to the floor.

The dinner, the people, the music were all gone – but the good smell remained.

Then Mrs. Potts remembered it was her very own turkey – unless that had been a dream too?

17

But no, there was the turkey, roasting quietly in its pan. She took a long sniff and then closed the oven door.

6

Mrs. Potts & Hugger
Have a Feast

IMAGINE! HER OWN daughter didn't recognize her. And that child. It had never occurred to her that she could have a grandchild and not even know it.

What a frightful dream. She picked up Hugger and held him tightly. Certainly she would never go to New York! The very idea was ridiculous. Anything could happen there!

Mrs. Potts was so pleased to be safely in her own home that she went around patting the pillows and smiling at her own reflection in the mirror.

It was morning now, and she said to Hugger, "You'll be hungry soon, I suppose."

Hugger meowed anxiously and rubbed against her legs.

"All right, all right," grumbled Mrs. Potts, but she wasn't really mad. She was hungry too.

So, she set to work preparing cranberry sauce, mashed potatoes, creamed onions, peas, and pumpkin pie until every burner on the stove was bubbling with good things, and the sink was piled with dirty pots and pans.

Mrs. Potts was pleased that she remembered the dishes her mother used to make and all the little special things that she had fixed for her own family years ago.

"Whew!" she said at last, when the dishes were done and the table was set for two.

"Now you'll see what Thanksgiving is all about," she told the cat. Hugger watched expectantly, while Mrs. Potts lit two candles. The light shone brightly in the cat's eyes.

Then she carefully carved the turkey and prepared a plate for each of them. Of course, Hugger was mostly interested in the turkey, but he got very small servings of the potatoes and peas because at Thanksgiving it's very important to have at least a taste of everything.

20

Then they sat down together and began to eat.

And eat and eat. Everything tasted so good, they both ate until they could hardly stand up.

After dinner Mrs. Potts sat down in her armchair and put her feet up, satisfied that she'd spent her holiday well. She had had a real Thanksgiving – not a frozen dinner – and she'd even had someone to share it with. She turned on the TV to see what was on – football, two Christmas movies, and a crime show. None of those interested her, so she turned the set off. She yawned. She'd had enough excitement for one day.

Hugger was already stretched out on his back, snoring contentedly. Even though it was only mid-afternoon, Mrs. Potts thought she deserved a nap.

But this time, she could not go to sleep.

She kept picturing those people lined up to eat dinner outside the church and the woman covered with newspapers in the parking lot of her office.

How cold they looked. How miserable.

"Wake up, Hugger!" she said at last. "We've got work to do."

7

Happy Thanksgiving, Mrs. Potts!

WHILE HUGGER WATCHED anxiously, Mrs. Potts began carving up that big turkey and putting it on plates. Then she heaped on gravy, cranberries, vegetables, and pie and wrapped the plates tightly in tin foil to keep the food warm.

When everything was ready, she loaded up the car. But once she had started down the street, she had misgivings. What was she doing? She had been watching too much television. She had been dreaming too many dreams. She was just an old lady with too much time on her hands.

Then she saw an old man shuffling down the street, his coat in tatters, his feet wrapped in plastic bags. Mrs. Potts slowed the car to a stop. She rolled down her window.

"Excuse me," she called. The man didn't even look up.

"How would you like some Thanksgiving dinner?" The old man glared at her as if she were crazy and said something mean.

Mrs. Potts blushed, but she didn't blame him. Even to herself she sounded silly. But what else should she say?

She closed the car window.

Maybe she should have just driven by and thrust the plate at him. Or dropped it out the window.

"No, no," she said to Hugger, "that wouldn't do."

She continued on down the block and saw another man and his dog huddled beside their shopping cart full of belongings. The man was playing the harmonica, and the tune reminded her of one that no-good musician wrote. In fact, it might have been the very one, but Mrs. Potts had never paid that much attention before.

She parked and got out of the car with two plates.

This man had a cup on the ground in front of him and did not look up as she approached him.

Mrs. Potts put a dollar in the cup, and then said, "I wonder if, perhaps you might . . . I have way more than I need – could I share it with you?" She lay the

23

plates down. The dog lifted his weary head and sniffed. Then his tail began to wag.

The man noticed the smell too and stopped playing. He looked up at Mrs. Potts. Then he lifted the tinfoil and took a deep whiff. Something hard and lonely went out of his face.

"This smells good," he said. "Thanks, lady."

"You're welcome," said Mrs. Potts, starting to hurry away. She couldn't think of anything else to say until she got into the car. Then she waved and called "Happy Thanksgiving!"

The man waved a drumstick after her, and the dog looked up from his plate just long enough to give a happy bark.

After that, it got easier. There were so many people who needed help – Mrs. Potts didn't have to look far to give away her dinners. In no time at all, there was only one left.

"I know where this one should go," Mrs. Potts said to Hugger and turned in the direction of her office.

It was beginning to get dark as she pulled into the parking lot next to her office building. There was the newspapery lump, just as she had seen it the night before. Mrs. Potts took the last dinner and hurried over to it. But this time the lump didn't move.

Mrs. Potts' heart started to pound. What if – ?

24

She came closer and realized that the lump was empty. It was only a pile of trash. The woman was gone.

Disappointed, she went back to the car. Then she saw the scrap of cardboard that had caught her attention the night before. In big blue wobbly letters it said "Happy Thanksgiving," but underneath had been added in thin spidery writing: Mrs. Potts!

"Happy Thanksgiving, Mrs. Potts!"

"Imagine that!" she said to Hugger. "That woman knew my name! She wished me a happy Thanksgiving and now she's gone. I may never see her again."

For a few minutes, Mrs. Potts stood on the spot thinking about the old woman and wished she had given her some money while she had the chance.

8

The Last Plate

ONE PLATE LEFT! thought Mrs. Potts as she started the car. She was still trying to decide where she should go next when the sign for Garden Street caught her eye. This was an address she had previously seen only on her payroll.

"Not much of a garden left here," she said to Hugger, as she drove past the rundown houses and pulled up at No. 45: a small gray house with one yellow light burning.

Before she could lose her nerve, Mrs. Potts went to the door and knocked.

There was a long wait, but finally Clara Thigg appeared. She looked as pale as ever in the porch light.

"Hello, Clara," said Mrs. Potts.

"Mrs. Potts?" Clara peered out into the darkness, a look of fear on her face. "Is something wrong? Has something happened at the office?"

Mrs. Potts chuckled. "No, no. It's a holiday, remember? No one works today."

Clara did not look reassured. "But then, why –"

"I didn't come to fire you, if that's what you're thinking," said Mrs. Potts gruffly.

Clara smiled, embarrassed. "Of course not. How silly of me. For a minute I did wonder."

"Mom –" a weak voice called from within, "Who's there?"

"We have a visitor, Abby," Clara called back. "Won't you come in?"

Mrs. Potts nodded, and Clara stepped aside to let her into the poorly furnished room. On the couch lay a little girl about seven years old bundled in blankets. She was even more pale and thin than her mother.

"You must be Abby," said Mrs. Potts, putting on a smile. She was ashamed to remember all the times she had thought Abby was not even real – just an excuse to get out of work.

Abby stared at Mrs. Potts.

"Abby, can't you say hello?" her mother asked.

Abby scowled and didn't answer.

"She's had the flu for more than a week now," explained Clara, "and today was a particularly bad day."

"What? No turkey dinner?"

"Oh no, she hasn't felt like eating."

28

"Not even pie?"

Clara shook her head.

"Well," said Mrs. Potts, with a satisfied smile. "Then I was right to come here after all."

Clara had just opened her mouth to say something, when Mrs. Potts got up and left.

She was even more surprised when her boss returned a few moments later, carrying the last plate. "I'm afraid you'll have to share," she said, "but I think there's enough for two."

She set the plate down on the table and pulled back the tinfoil. The smell of turkey filled the air.

"O-o-h," sighed Clara.

"O-o-h," said Abby. Her eyes brightened, and she pushed herself up against her pillows. "I think I might be hungry," she announced.

"Of course, you are. It's Thanksgiving. Everyone is hungry on Thanksgiving."

So, Mrs. Potts fixed them each a plate. Then Clara and Abby ate and ate until they too were stuffed, and the pink had come into their cheeks.

9

Mrs. Potts & Hugger
Make Some Friends

WHEN THEY WERE through eating, Abby wanted Mrs. Potts to meet her doll Agatha, and Mrs. Potts was quite amazed that she remembered well how to talk to dolls.

Clara sat knitting a scarf for Abby and smiling at them.

"You know I would have sworn that you didn't believe in Thanksgiving – or any other holiday," she said.

"Exactly," said Mrs. Potts. "But that was yesterday, and today is today."

"What happened?" asked Abby.

Mrs. Potts had to stop and think.

"I guess it all started with Hugger – or was it the lump of newspapers?"

"A mugger?" Abby's eyes widened.

"Oh no, not mugger. Hugger," said Mrs. Potts, bending down to look in her purse. "Here he is," she said, pulling out the cat. "This is Hugger."

Hugger yawned and looked around him.

Abby gave a happy yelp.

"A cat! Oh, Mom! Can I hold him?"

"Of course," said Mrs. Potts, depositing the cat in Abby's lap. "He's very friendly."

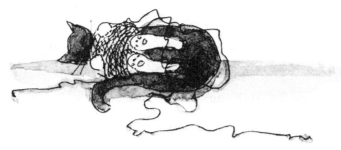

Then Mrs. Potts and Clara watched while Hugger and Abby made friends and began a game that involved a piece of Clara's yarn and a lot of whooping and laughing.

Mrs. Potts thought Abby's laugh was one of the nicest sounds she had ever heard. Really, she was a very pretty child when she didn't look so sour. Even Clara looked prettier at home than she did at the office. Of course, Mrs. Potts had to admit that she had hardly ever looked at Clara before. She had been too busy giving her orders. Now they got acquainted. Clara talked about how sad Abby had been ever since her father died a year ago – and how wonderful it was to see her having fun.

Mrs. Potts found herself sharing stories about Lucy and her own past that she hadn't told anyone in years.

"I used to hide under the piano with my cat," she said, "but Lucy was very outgoing. She had a cheerful disposition even as a baby."

Clara listened attentively, but the more often Mrs. Potts mentioned Lucy's name the more restless she became.

Finally, she stood up.

"Abby, Clara," she said, "Hugger and I have to go now."

Abby reluctantly gave up her game and came to the door with Hugger. "You will come back, won't you?" she asked. "Soon?"

Mrs. Potts looked at Clara, embarrassed.

"If you'd like me to," she said.

Clara smiled and held out her hand, "Of course, we would. You've made our Thanksgiving a very happy one."

Mrs. Potts blushed. "I've had a good time too," she said.

Then she gave Clara a hug. Mrs. Potts was not used to hugging people, so she was a little awkward, but Clara understood what she meant. Then Abby and Mrs. Potts hugged. And everyone hugged Hugger, who meowed.

10

Mrs. Potts Finds a Family

WHEN MRS. POTTS arrived back at her apartment, everything looked different. Instead of an empty silent place, it seemed filled with voices. Not television voices, but real voices. Clara. Abby. Hugger. Lucy.

She kicked off her shoes and stared at the phone. Hugger watched her curiously.

She knew what she wanted to do. It was just a matter of doing it.

Bravely she picked up the telephone and dialed. Far away it rang and rang until finally a woman answered: "Hello?"

For a moment, Mrs. Potts thought she had the wrong number.

"Hello, this is Martha Potts. I am trying to reach –" she began.

But before she could continue, the woman said:

"Mom! I can't believe it's you!"

"Why not? I hope I always return my calls."

"Mom – it really *is* you!" Lucy laughed. "Harry – it's Mom!"

Then a man came on and said "Hi, Mom!" which Mrs. Potts thought was a totally inappropriate way for a stranger to address her.

"Are you going to come for Christmas?" asked Lucy.

"No," said Mrs. Potts severely. "It's out of the question."

"Oh," said Lucy, sounding disappointed.

"All that snow and ice are beautiful for television, but I'm too old for that. If you want to see me, then you and –"

"Harry –"

"And Harry will have to come out here and spend Christmas with me. If you would like," she added a bit more hesitantly.

"We'd love to, Mom."

"Really? You would?" Mrs. Potts was taken aback. For a moment she wondered what she had gotten herself into, but then she said: "Good." And she meant it.

II

A Strange Warm Feeling

AT LAST MRS. Potts was ready to go to bed. She put on her nightgown and turned out the lights.

Hugger climbed up beside her and started to purr.

"Beggar," she said, stroking his head.

It had been a very, very long day. She could hardly even remember the last time she'd slept in her bed. As she thought about all the things that had happened, a strange warm feeling crept over her. At first, she didn't recognize it – she wondered if she might be coming down with a cold.

But then she realized what it was.

She was grateful. For her warm little apartment and her new cat, for her daughter Lucy and Harry the no-good musician, for Clara and Abby, and for the all the people she'd met that day.

She savored the feeling like the smell of roasting turkey.

"What's the world coming to?" Mrs. Potts said under her breath. And then she laughed in the darkness.

"A Happy Thanksgiving," she whispered and went to sleep.

The end.

ALICE K. BOATWRIGHT is the author of the award-winning Ellie Kent mysteries and other fiction. She was formerly program director for a children's museum, and her writing for children has been published in *Cricket*. She lives with her husband and three cats near Seattle. (PHOTO: MARIA ARAGON)

JAN L. WALDRON is a widely collected artist and the author of *John Pig's Halloween*, *Angel Pig and the Hidden Christmas*, and two memoirs. She lives on the New Hampshire seacoast with her husband and cat. (PHOTO: DAVID McPHAIL)

Firefly Ink
BOOKS

Firefly Ink Books was established to publish stories for families and friends to read together. The name was inspired by a memory of my own family sitting on the back porch on a summer night, watching the fireflies soar and blink as we told each other stories.

I hope you enjoyed our inaugural book, *Mrs. Potts Finds Thanksgiving.* And, if you did, please pass the news on.

To stay in touch with what we are doing, please visit

WWW.FIREFLYINKBOOKS.COM

Alice K. Boatwright
Founder & Publisher

Made in the USA
Monee, IL
03 November 2022

17064986R00026